The Pancake

ANITA LOBEL

Greenwillow
Read-alone

GREENWILLOW BOOKS
A Division of William Morrow & Company, Inc.
New York

Library of Congress Cataloging in Publication Data
Lobel, Anita. The pancake.
(Greenwillow Read-alone books)
Summary: A rolling pancake eludes all its
pursuers except one clever pig.
[1. Folklore—Danish] I. Title. PZ8.1.L93Pan [398.2] [E]
77-24970   ISBN 0-688-80125-0   ISBN 0-688-84125-2 lib. bdg.

Once there was a woman

who had seven hungry children.

She cooked them a pancake.

It lay in the pan

and swelled and rose

and grew thick and tempting.

The children stood

around the stove.

They could not wait

to taste the pancake.

"Please, mother," they cried,

"let us eat the pancake right away!

We are so hungry."

"Wait, my dear ones,"

said the woman.

"Before we eat,

I must flip the pancake over

and cook it on the other side."

When the pancake heard
that it was to be eaten,
it jumped out of the pan
and rolled like a wheel
through the door
and onto the road.

"Wait, wait," cried the woman.
"My children are hungry.
Do not run away from us!"
The woman ran after the pancake
with the pan in one hand
and the spoon in the other.
The seven children ran after her.
"Catch it! Grab it! Hold it!"
the children shouted.
But the pancake rolled faster
and faster down the road.
Soon the woman and the children
were left far behind.

After a while, the pancake met
a farmer. "Good day, farmer,"
said the pancake as it rolled by.
"Good day, pancake," said the farmer.
"You look good enough to eat.
Do not roll away so quickly.
Stop and let me have
a bite out of you!"

"If I can roll away from

the woman who cooked me,

and her seven children

who wanted to eat me,

I can roll away from you too,

dumb farmer," said the pancake.

And off it rolled.

Soon it met a goose.

"Good day, goose," said the pancake.

"Good day, pancake," said the goose.

"You look very delicious.

Do not roll away so quickly.

Stop and let me take

a bite out of you."

"If I can roll away from
the woman who cooked me,
and her seven children
who wanted to eat me,
and a dumb farmer
who wanted to take
a bite out of me,
I can roll away from you too,
silly goose," said the pancake.
And off it rolled.

Soon it met a cat.

"Good day, cat," said the pancake.

"Good day, pancake," said the cat.

"You look very tasty. Do not roll

away so quickly. Stop and let me

take a bite out of you."

"If I can roll away from

the woman who cooked me,

and her seven children

who wanted to eat me,

a dumb farmer

and a silly goose

who wanted to take

a bite out of me,

I can roll away from you too,

stupid cat," said the pancake.

And off it rolled.

The pancake rolled and rolled.

Soon it met a sheep.

"Good day, sheep,"

said the pancake.

"Good day, pancake," said the sheep.
"You look very sweet. Do not roll
away so quickly. Stop and let me
take a bite out of you."

"If I can roll away from

the woman who cooked me,

and her seven children

who wanted to eat me,

a dumb farmer

and a silly goose

and a stupid cat who wanted

to take a bite out of me,

I can roll away from you too,

foolish sheep," said the pancake.

And off it rolled.

The pancake kept on rolling
down the road.
Soon it met a goat.
"Good day, goat,"
  said the pancake.
"Good day, pancake,"
  said the goat.
"You look very crunchy.
  Do not roll away so quickly.
  Stop and let me take a bite
  out of you."

"If I can roll away from
the woman who cooked me,
and her seven children
who wanted to eat me,
a dumb farmer
and a silly goose
and a stupid cat
and a foolish sheep
who wanted to take
a bite out of me,
I can roll away from you too,
old goat," said the pancake.
And off it rolled.

The pancake came to a brook.

By the brook stood a pig.

"Good day, pig," said the pancake.

"Good day, pancake," said the pig.

What a mouth-watering pancake,

thought the pig.

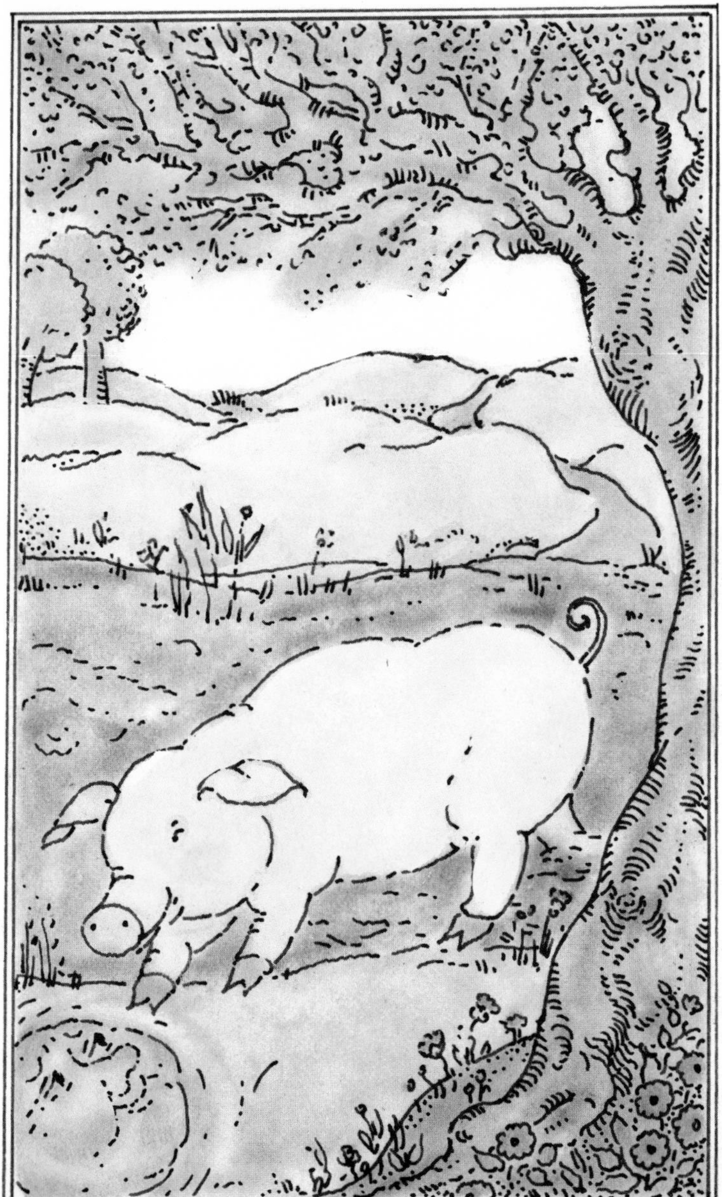

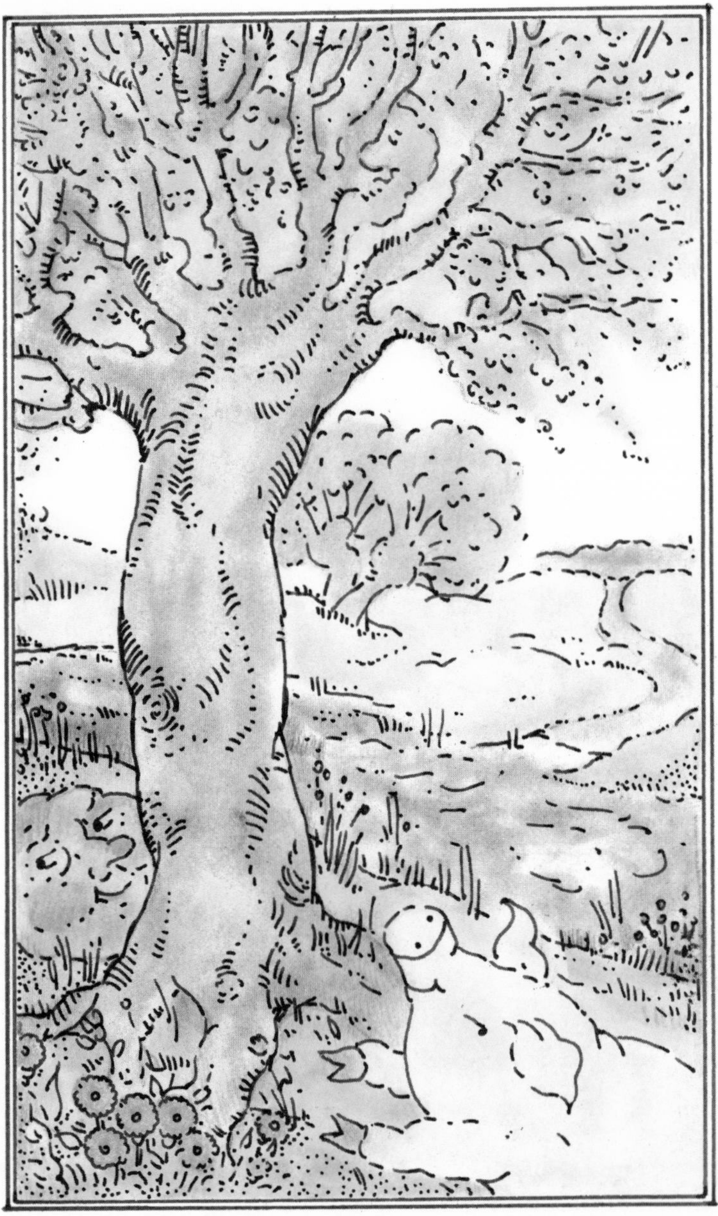

"I have rolled away from

the woman who cooked me,

and her seven children

who wanted to eat me,

a dumb farmer,

a silly goose,

a stupid cat,

a foolish sheep,

and an old goat

who all wanted bites out of me,"

bragged the pancake to the pig.

"I should be able to get across

this brook without becoming

wet and soggy!"

"I will help you," said the pig.

"Just sit on the tip of my nose and

  I will take you to the other side."

  How clever of me to meet

  such a kind pig, thought the pancake

  and rolled onto the pig's nose.

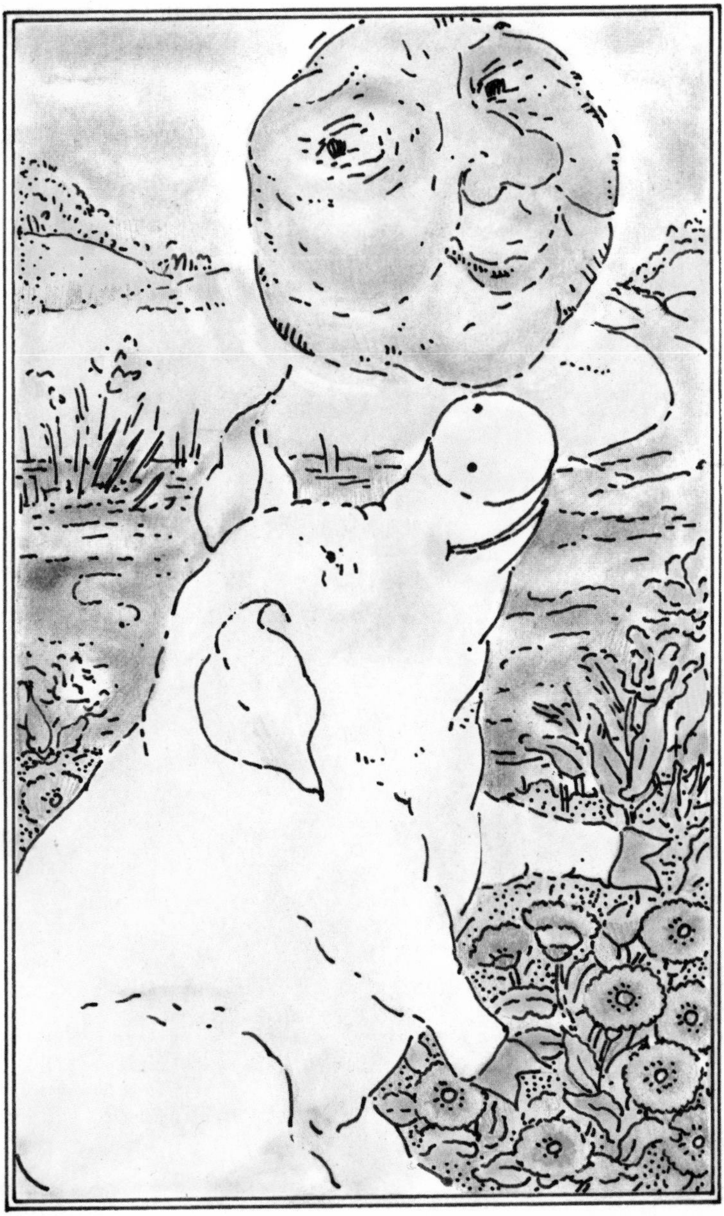

"Oink, oink," said the pig
and swallowed the pancake
in one large gulp.

By then, the woman,

the children,

the farmer,

the goose,

the cat,

the sheep,

and the goat

came running to the brook

where the pig was resting.

"Have you seen a pancake roll by?"

said the woman to the pig.

"Did you make

that wonderful pancake?"

said the pig.

"It was the best I ever ate!"

"You ate our pancake!"
cried the children.
"And we are so hungry!"

"I know what to do,"

    their mother said.

"We shall all go home now.

    And I will make

    an even better pancake

    for everybody."

"A splendid idea," said the pig.

    So the children,

    the farmer,

    the goose,

    the cat,

    the sheep,

    the goat,

    and the pig

    followed the woman home.

There she cooked
the best pancake
she had ever made.
And they ate it
before it could roll away.